JOHN W. SCHAUM
POPULAR PIANO PIECES

Edited by
JOHN W. SCHAUM

Arranged by
WESLEY SCHAUM

Illustrations by Jeannette Aquino

PRE-A

THE GREEN BOOK

Exclusive Distributors
IMP
International Music Publications
Southend Road, Woodford Green, Essex IG8 8HN, England.
Photocopying of this copyright material is illegal.

Editor: Carole Flatau
Production Coordinator: David C. Olsen

FOREWORD

The purpose of the **JOHN W. SCHAUM PIANO COURSE** is:

1. **TO TEACH PIANO** in the most natural and the happiest way.
2. **TO PRESENT** technical information accurately and progressively.
3. **NOT TO DEFINE** the scope of Grade I - or Grade II - or any other grades.
4. **NOT TO CONFINE** the intellectual range of the pupil within the first year or any other period of time.
5. **BUT TO OFFER** a gradual and progressive pedagogic continuity through a series of books named Pre-A, A, B, C, D.
6. **LEADING** to the eventual mastery of the instrument.

The POPULAR PIANO PIECES books correspond with the traditional Course books, providing the student with additional material to reinforce the musical understanding and keyboard skills acquired through study of the Course books.

Each piece has been carefully selected and carefully arranged to capture and retain the interest of the performer and the listener. The solo arrangements are complete and satisfying; the duet accompaniments add harmonic and rhythmic flavor.

CONTENTS

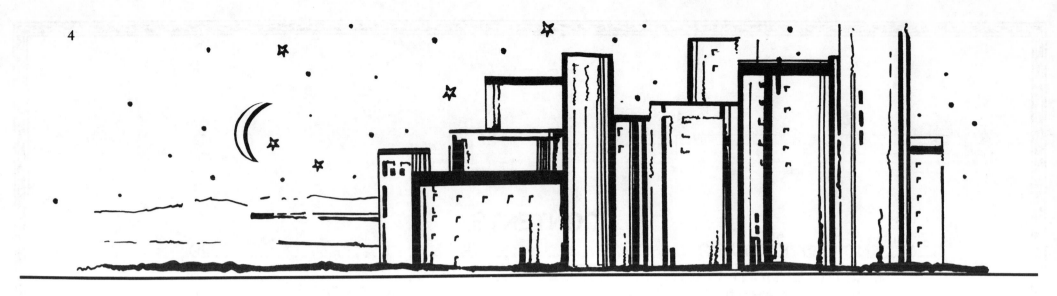

THE HILL STREET BLUES THEME

Music by MIKE POST
Arr. by Wesley Schaum

Duet Accompaniment

YOU LIGHT UP MY LIFE

Words and Music by
JOE BROOKS
Arr. by Wesley Schaum

You light up my life. You give me hope,

to car - ry on. You light up my days and fill my

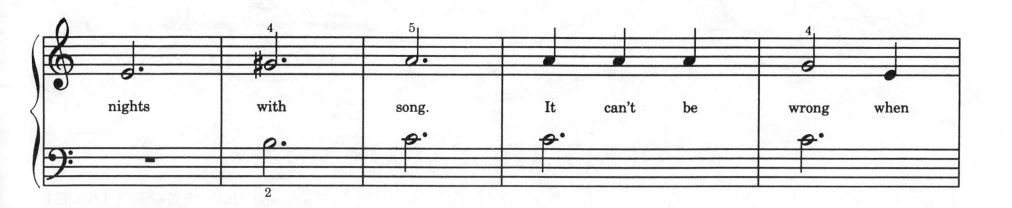

nights   with   song.   It   can't   be   wrong   when

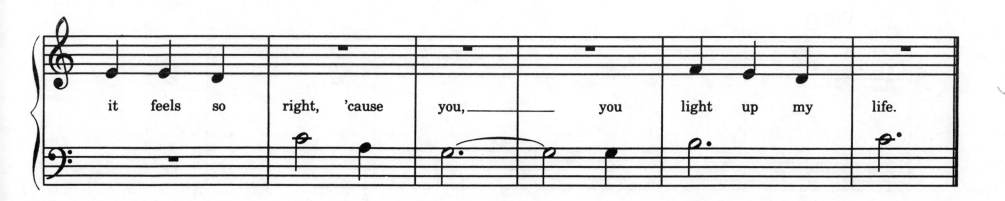

it   feels   so   right,   'cause   you, _____ you   light   up   my   life.

Duet Accompaniment

I'M POPEYE THE SAILOR MAN

Words and Music by SAMMY LERNER
Arr. by Wesley Schaum

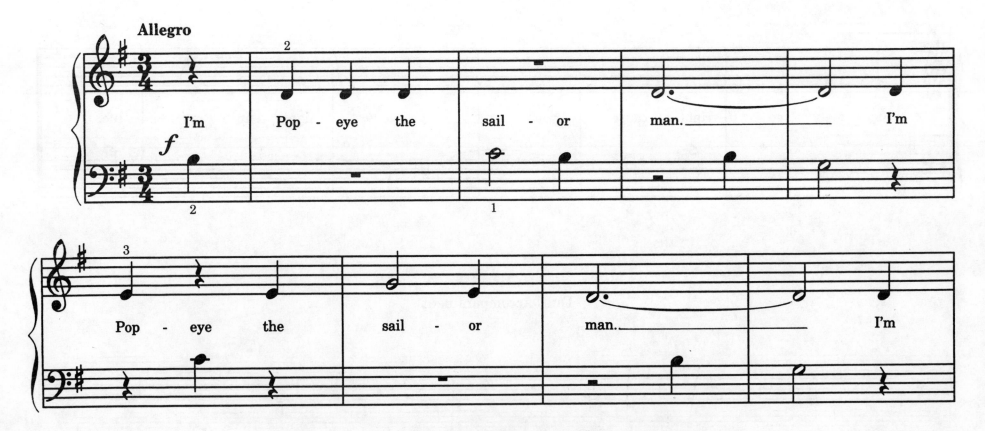

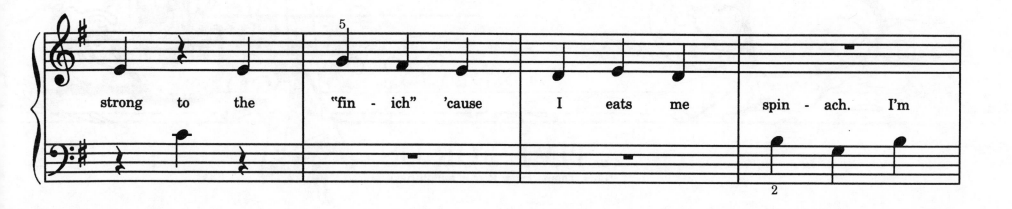

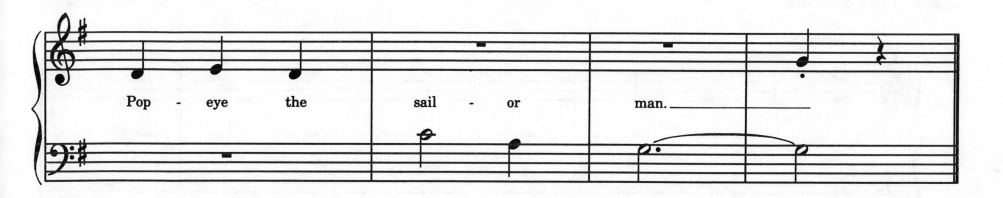

Duet Accompaniment

A TIME FOR US
(Love Theme From Romeo and Juliet)

Words by LARRY KUSIK
and EDDIE SNYDER

Music by NINO ROTA
Arr. by Wesley Schaum

A time for us through tears and thorns

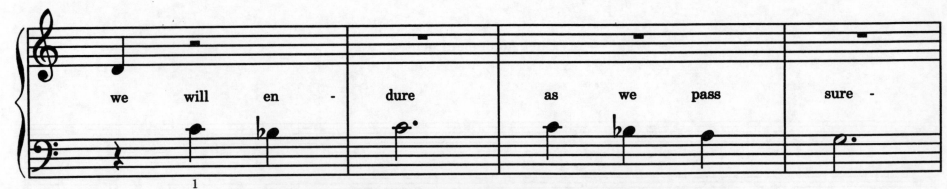

we will en - dure as we pass sure -

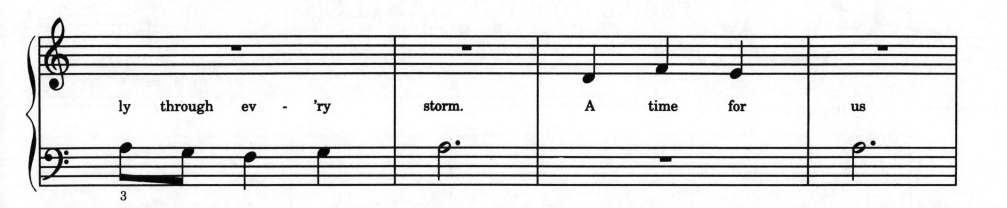

Duet Accompaniment

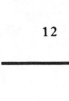

Theme from ICE CASTLES
(Through the Eyes of Love)

Lyrics by CAROLE BAYER SAGER

Music by MARVIN HAMLISCH
Arr. by Wesley Schaum

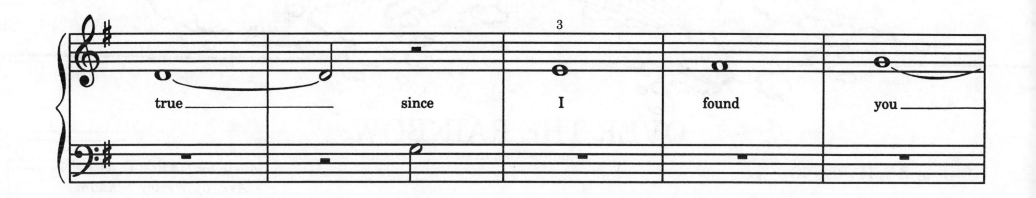

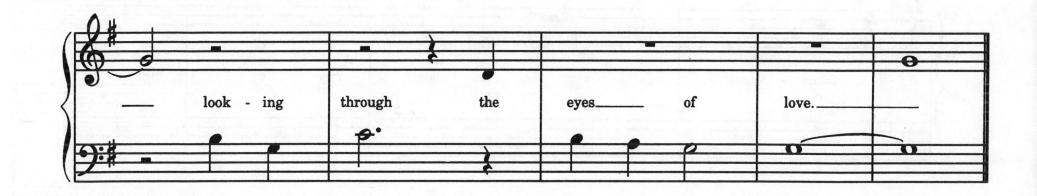

Duet Accompaniment

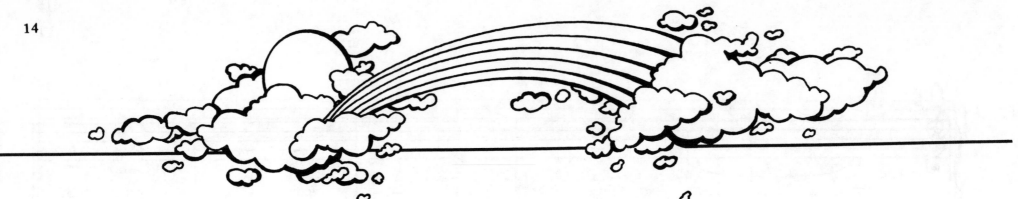

OVER THE RAINBOW

(from "The Wizard of Oz")

Lyric by E.Y. HARBURG

Music by HAROLD ARLEN
Arr. by Wesley Schaum

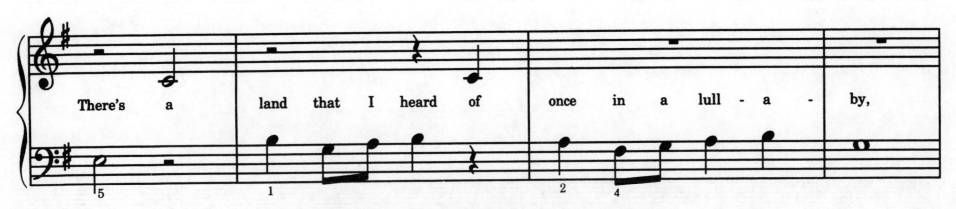

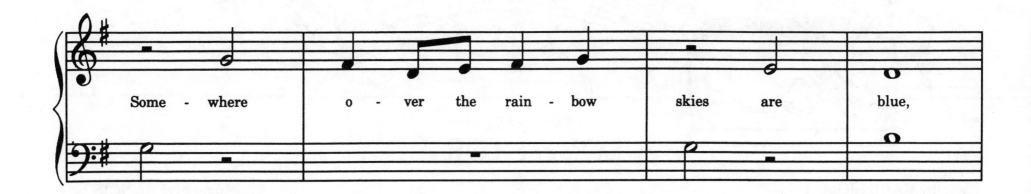

Some - where   o - ver the rain - bow   skies are   blue,

And   the   dreams that you dare to   dream real - ly do come   true.

Duet Accompaniment

(Where Do I Begin)

LOVE STORY

Lyric by CARL SIGMAN

Music by FRANCIS LAI
Arr. by Wesley Schaum

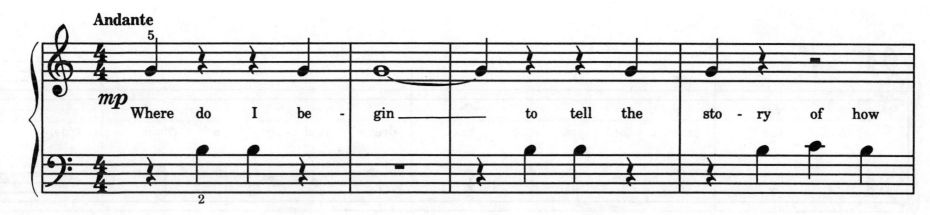

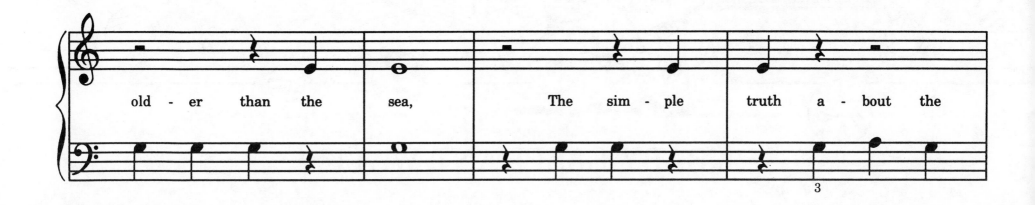

old - er than the   sea,   The   sim - ple   truth a - bout the

love   she   brings   to   me? _____   Where   do   I   start?

Duet Accompaniment

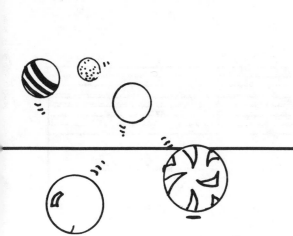

BABY ELEPHANT WALK

By HENRY MANCINI
Arr. by Wesley Schaum

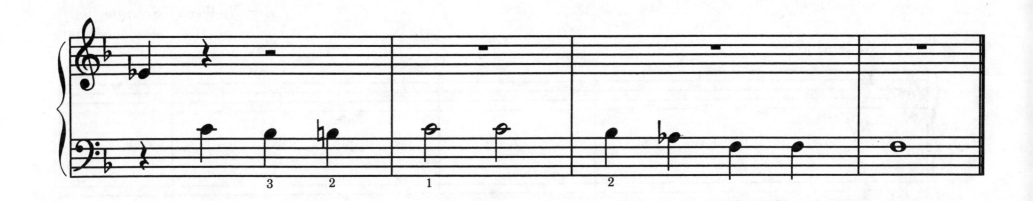

Duet Accompaniment

AND I LOVE YOU SO

Words and Music by DON McLEAN
Arr. by Wesley Schaum

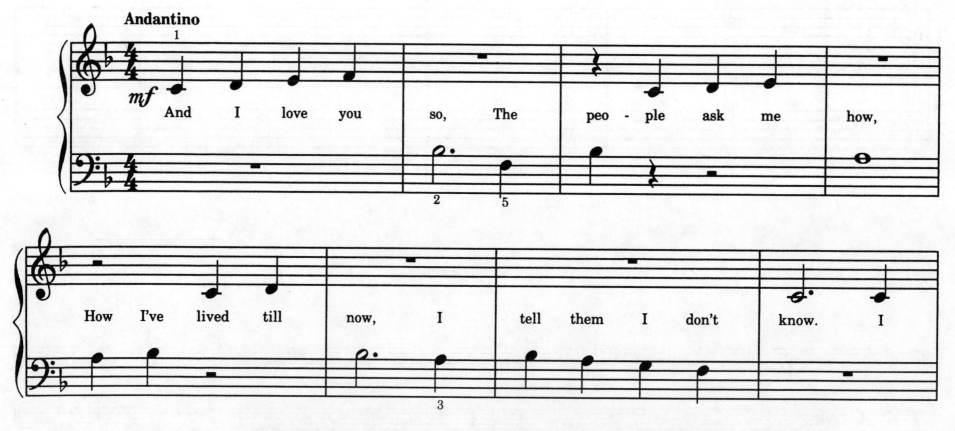

And I love you so, The peo - ple ask me how, How I've lived till now, I tell them I don't know. I

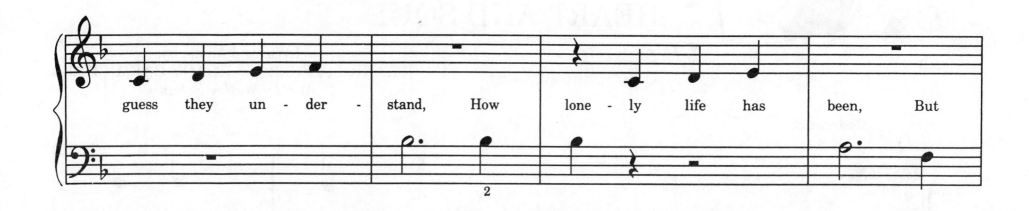

guess they un - der - stand, How lone - ly life has been, But

life be - gan a - gain, The day you took my hand.

Duet Accompaniment

HEART AND SOUL

Lyric and Music by
FRANK LOESSER and **HOAGY CARMICHAEL**
Arr. by Wesley Schaum

Moderato

Heart and soul ___ I fell in love with you. Heart and soul ___

___ the way a fool would do, Mad - ly be - cause you held me

Duet Accompaniment